Deirdre Coates

At Home With SPELLING 2

OXFORD

UNIVERSITY PRESS

Introduction

The *At Home With* workbooks introduce and reinforce key numeracy and literacy concepts for primary school children. They provide lots of opportunities to develop the key skills that are the basis of primary school curriculum work. The workbooks are available in three levels: 3–5 years, 5–7 years, and 7–9 years. The activities are fun and are designed to stimulate discussion, as well as practical skills. Some children will be able to complete the activities alone, after initial discussion; others may benefit from adult support throughout. All children will enjoy rewarding themselves with a sticker when they reach the end of an activity.

Using the book

At Home With Spelling 2 offers a variety of activities which focus, in particular, on the following skills:

- recognizing common word structures
- understanding spelling patterns
- knowing when to use double consonants
- hearing the difference between long and short vowels and knowing how this influences spelling
- decoding unfamiliar words.

OXFORD
UNIVERSITY PRESS

Great Clarendon Street, Oxford OX2 6DP

Oxford University Press is a department of the University of Oxford.

Oxford is a registered trade mark of Oxford University Press
in the UK and in certain other countries

© Deirdre Coates 1997
Illustrations by Ray and Corinne Burrows

The moral rights of the author have been asserted

Database right Oxford University Press (maker)

First published 1997
Reissued 2009
This edition 2012

All rights reserved.

You must not circulate this book in any other binding or cover
and you must impose this same condition on any acquirer

British Library Cataloguing in Publication Data

Data available

ISBN: 978 0 19 273336 8

10 9 8 7 6 5 4 3 2 1

Printed in China

Paper used in the production of this book is a natural, recyclable product made
from wood grown in sustainable forests. The manufacturing process conforms
to the environmental regulations of the country of origin.

Contents

Vowels

The vowels that say their sound are called short vowels.

a	e	i	o	u
apple	egg	igloo	orange	umbrella

Ring all the short vowels in these words.

bag   beg   big   bog   bug
hat   hit   hot   hut
tennis   trumpet   lipstick
rabbit   napkin   bandit

The vowels that say their name are called long vowels.

a	e	i	o	u
ape	even	ice	open	Union Jack

Ring all the long vowels in these words.

cake   like   these   hope   tube
me   go   pine   lane   hose
tune   no   five   mile   rule   pole

The magic vowel rocket

If e comes at the end of a word it makes the vowel in front say its name.
Think of the e as a rocket that can jump over the consonant and change the vowel sound.

hop

hope

as in orange

as in open

this   Add e and change   this

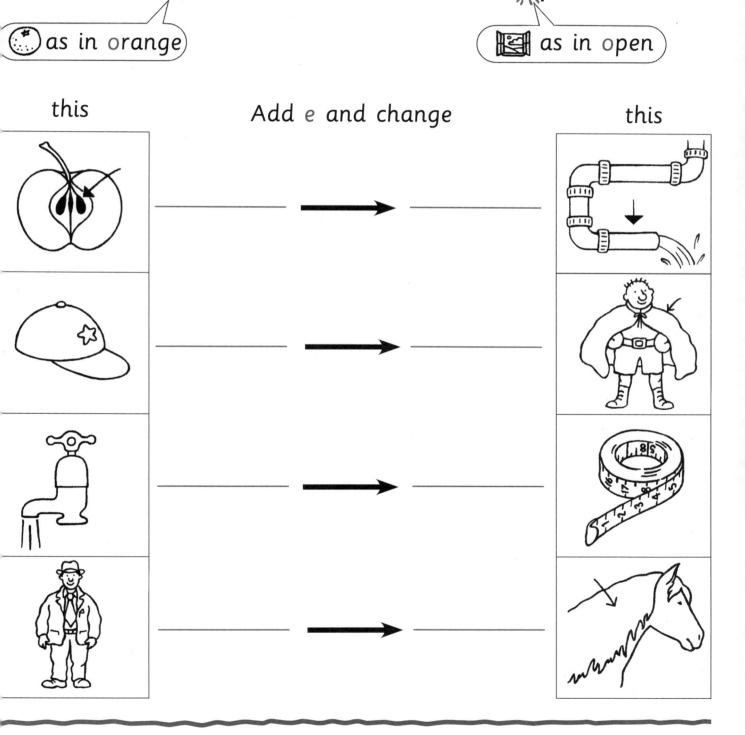

Long and short vowels

Fill each gap with the right word. Choose between the long and short vowels.

rid
ride
quit
quite
mad
made
Tim
time
not
note
cub
cube
tub
tube
lick
like
bit
bite

I want to get _____ of my bike. I don't want to

_____ any more.

I am _____ sure I want to _____ the bike club.

I got _____ when they _____ us wash our bikes

every week. Perhaps it's _____ I gave it to my

brother _____. Or, if I sold it, I might get a nice big

_____. I'm _____ sure what I would do with all

that money. I could buy a lion _____ which I would

feed with a _____ of sugar, a _____ of ice

cream and a _____ of chocolate spread. I would

_____ him to _____ my hand but I would not

like him to _____ me one little _____.

I think I'll keep my bike. It may be safer.

-ore

In -ore words the -e has a rest and doesn't change the vowel sound.

Read the story and put all the -ore words you find into the store cupboard at the end.

The Snorer

My dad swore that he would not snore any more. So before he went to bed he took an apple from the store and ate it till just the core was left. He put this under his bed. Then he wore a peg on his nose and tore up an old cloth, wet it, and put it over his mouth. He thought this would be a magic cure. Then he got into bed and went to sleep.

In the morning he asked mum, "What's the score?"

"It was a bore," she replied. "The snores were even worse. And what is this apple core doing under the bed? Tonight you can go down to the sea shore to sleep. Then only the fish and birds will hear you."

The Word Store

–are

In -are words the -e makes the vowel sound a bit different from its name:

Take care
of this car.

Do the -are crossword and find the answers in this list:

bare   fare   stare   beware
care   hare   scare   square
dare   mare   spare

Across

3 A female horse

5 To feel concerned

7 Be careful!

8 To look hard and long at someone or something

9 The money paid by people who travel on public transport

Down

1 Without clothes

2 To be brave enough to do something

4 To frighten

6 An animal like a large rabbit

8 Something extra or left over

ck k

k can't stand alone after a short vowel, so c has to stand between.

back peck pick pocket puck

But k can stand alone after long vowels and consonants.

silk walk bank blink bark folk
cake speak bike spoke like

Sort these words under ck for a short vowel; and k for a long vowel or consonant.

think	cake	pick	sack	deck
desk	bike	take	brick	sock
luck	bank	bake	back	quick
peck	pink	buck	truck	trunk

ck	**k**

ck word quiz

Write a ck word by each of the arrows.

ck or k

Remember that k after a short vowel has to be -ck.

Ring the right spelling in each box.

blac (black)	cacke cake	bunks buncks
blak blakk	cace cack	buncs bucks
drinck drink	clockt clok clock	sunck sunk sunc sunkk	stic stik stick
inck ink	racke rake	pocker poker	sik sick
sinck sink	bice bike bicke	tiket ticket	pocket poket

y

y at the end of a word acts like a vowel.
In all these words y has a long i sound.

by	dry	try	rely
my	shy	why	occupy
fly	sky	July	multiply
fry	spy	reply	satisfy

cry

Ring all the words where y sounds like a long i.

My little sister is very shy. I can't think why. If you speak to her she will not reply. If a fly from the sky lands on her hand she begins to cry. Her face is never dry and she will not try to stop.

Fill the gaps with -y words.

1 If you are alone you are all _____ yourself.

2 The month that follows June is _____ .

3 I _____ with _____ little eye.

4 Birds and insects use their wings to _____ .

5 If you are wet you use a towel to get _____ .

-oy

Read about annoying Roy and put all the -oy words you find into the toy cupboard.

On Saturday Roy came to play. He is a very bad boy. It seems to give him joy to destroy things. Mum told us to go to my room and find some toys to play with. He pushed me into the fort and broke the flag. Then he threw my ball out of the window. He does not enjoy playing with things, just destroying them. He broke my trumpet and banged and banged on the drum. Mum came in and said, "What a racket!" Then she saw the mess. "You bad boys! Are you trying to annoy me? I will need to employ someone to mend all these toys."

Then she sent Roy home and told him to stay there.

-ay

Finish the rhymes with -ay words.

day

way

dismay

hay

tray

pay

stray

may

I must go, I cannot stay

Perhaps I'll come another _____ .

The toy with which I like to play,

That little girl has thrown _____ .

The small black hen began to sway

And then an egg I saw her _____ .

She asked to get without delay

Her tea and cake upon a _____ .

Now that it's the month of May,

The farmers will be making _____ .

He threw his hands up in dismay,

The bill has come, he cannot _____ .

She falls down on her knees to pray

Let's go to the sea for our _____ .

today

sway

play

delay

lay

bay

stay

clay

spray

yesterday   betray   day   birthday

holiday   away   say

The days of the week

Sunday

Monday

Tuesday

Wednesday

Thursday

Friday

Saturday

Write out the days with a u in them.

_____

Which day has 3 syllables?

_____

How many days have an a in them?

_____

Tom asks Sam to play on the only day that has two a's in it.
Which day is that?

_____

_____

Who's who?

Look out for the oo words! Write each name in the right box.

1   Jill is in a bad mood.

2   Jack likes to cook and has his best spoon with him.

3   Wanda is looking for her broomstick.

4 Tess needs to get to the bathroom very soon.

5 Bill likes food too much.

6 Sam is on his way to the swimming pool. He has hurt his foot.

7 Molly has her boots on because she is going fishing in the brook.

8 Ben is a carpenter and has all his tools with him.

9 Ann thinks she looks good.

10 Tom's mum took him to the fair and he has a big balloon.

11 Jim is on his way to school.

12 May has a pain in her tooth and must go to the dentist.

13 Harry has been for a run and needs a cool drink.

14 John is always reading a book. He'd better look out or he may fall over.

15 The man in the moon is called Nick.

oo

oo can make two sounds. One is a long one like the oo in spoon. One is a short one like the oo in book.

Sort these words into long oo under spoon, and short oo under book.

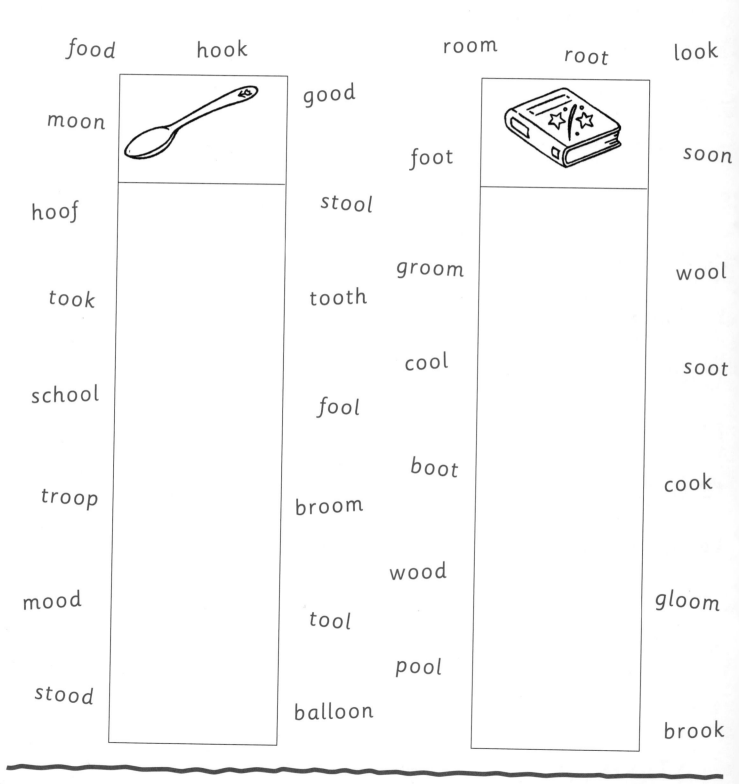

food   hook   room   root   look

                                    good

moon   foot   soon

hoof   stool

                                        groom   wool

took   tooth

                                        cool   soot

school   fool

                                        boot   cook

troop   broom

                                        wood

mood   tool   gloom

                                        pool

stood   balloon

                                                          brook

ee

Lots of words have *ee* in them. Here are some:

sleep	fleet	tree	seen	knee
deep	need	free	been	peel
sheep	deed	flee	keen	wheel
weep	feed	knee	queen	beech
sweep	weed	three	between	speech
keep	seed	agree	teeth	sneeze
sweet	week	coffee	eel	breeze
feet	cheek	see	heel	cheer

Peep through the key holes. What *ee* words do you see?

_____   _____   _____

_____   _____   _____

_____   _____   _____

ow

Read the story, and write all the ow words
you find in the tower.

OW

On the day the circus came to town,
a big crowd gathered to watch the
parade. Everyone was happy. There
was not a frown to be seen on any
face.

A clown came first, leading a brown
cow with a garland of flowers round
her neck and a gold crown on her
brow. Then came the strong man.
He towered above the crowd. How
powerful he looked and the people
cowered before him. Then came the
lady acrobats with towels around their
necks and powder on their faces.
Next came the lion tamer with his four
lions. No one was allowed to come
near. Their growls drowned the howls
made by the crowd. Last of all came
the birdman. You could hardly see him
because he was covered with owls and
fowls of every kind. Everyone vowed
they would see the circus that night.

Suddenly the sky grew dark and the
rain came down. This was more than a
shower. We ran for cover, afraid that
we might drown.

1 What was the clown leading?

_____

2 Why could they not see the birdman?

_____

3 What did the acrobats have on their faces?

_____

4 What noises did the lions make?

_____

5 How do we know that the strong man was tall?

_____

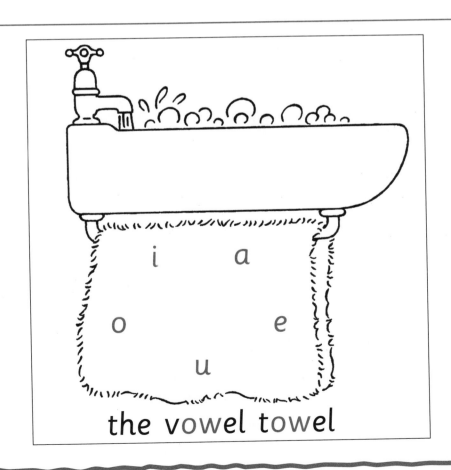

the vowel towel

Double consonants

Remember the magic vowel rocket from page 5. It jumps over a consonant and makes the vowel in front into a long vowel sound. At the end of a word, y counts as a vowel.

 evil   hope   pipe   human

If you want to keep the vowel sound short, double the middle consonant, so that the rocket can't reach the vowel in front.

ladder   pillow   funny   letter

Ring the right word.

| leter   letter | spider   spidder | lader   ladder | coma   comma |

1 We had a [super/supper] time at Sally's party.

2 Last night we had [super/supper] at Granny's house.

3 I like lots of [buter/butter] on my toast.

4 It is [later/latter] than I thought so we had [beter/better] go home.

Double the last letter

You follow the same double consonant rule when you change a word by adding a suffix:

-ing   -er   -ed   -est   -en   -y

If the base word ends in a short vowel and one consonant, double the consonant and add the suffix.

hop + ing = hopping

mad + er   = madder

skip + ed = skipped

sad + est = saddest

fat   + en = fatten

mud + y   = muddy

If you did not double the consonant the 2nd vowel would send over its rocket to make the first vowel say its name.

Read these words and put a ring round the base words.

(swim)ming   hotter

                              begging

   foggy   biggest

fatter   hopped

          sunny

  slipping   flipped

What are they doing?

Write down the base word, then add the suffix -ing.

wag

wagging

-ed

Write out these sentences with the verb in the past tense.
Are the vowel sounds short or long?

Today he skips to school.

Yesterday he _____

Today I slip on a banana skin.

Yesterday I _____

Today I spot my friend in the street.

Yesterday I _____

Today we pin roses to our jackets.

Yesterday we _____

Today I shop in the supermarket.

Yesterday I _____

Today we clap the clown who is funny.

Yesterday _____

Today you pat the dog on the head.

Yesterday _____

Today we chat to each other.

Yesterday _____

–er –est

Now adjectives: is the vowel sound short or long?

sad   sadder   saddest

fat   _____   _____

hot   _____   _____

thin   _____   _____

big   _____   _____

Take off the -e

We are going to add these same suffixes to different words.

-ing   -er   -ed   -est   -en   -y

If the base word ends in -e, take off the -e and add the suffix.
Remember, at the end of a word, y counts as a vowel.

hope + ing = hoping
hope + ed = hoped
take + er = taker
take + en = taken
brave + est = bravest
rose + y = rosy

Look at these words with suffixes and single middle consonants.
Write their base words beside them.

liking	like	riding	_____
taken	_____	blamed	_____
riper	_____	driver	_____
lived	_____	wisest	_____
finest	_____	cared	_____
freezer	_____	hoping	_____
hating	_____	shaken	_____

—er —est

Write out these adjectives.

wise

The owl is the _____ of all the birds.

white

Sam's shirt is _____ than Jim's.

Jim

Sam

pale

Grey is _____ than black, but white is
_____ of all.

brave

Ann

Jill

Jill is

_____ than Ann.

wide

Tom

Mary

Jack

Mary's smile is _____ than Tom's. Jack has the
_____ smile of all.

What are they doing?

Write down the base word, then the word with the suffix -ing.

smile

smiling

Compound words

A compound word is made from two words put together.
Write a compound word next to each picture.

railway

_____

_____

_____

_____

_____

_____

_____

_____

_____

Word sums

Join the two parts to make words of two syllables.

am	+	 bush	=	_____
con	+	(tent)	=	_____
10	+	nis	=	_____
sel	+	(fish)	=	_____
up	+	(hill)	=	_____

ab + _____ = _____

un + _____ = _____

us + _____ = _____

ib + _____ = _____

vin + _____ = _____

bit
band
dow
set
bon

Dictionary time

Look up car- in the Oxford Junior Dictionary
and fill in the answers.

1	c	a	r					
2	c	a	r					
3	c	a	r					
4	c	a	r					
5	c	a	r					
6	c	a	r					
7	c	a	r					
8	c	a	r					
9	c	a	r					
10	c	a	r					

car

1 Thick paper
2 Goods carried by a ship
3 A small plastic or cardboard box
4 Thick fabric for covering the floor
5 An orange vegetable that is long and pointed at one end
6 A funny drawing often seen in a comic or made into a film
7 A small house on wheels that can be pulled by cars
8 A knitted jacket
9 A festive occasion when there are parades, fairs and lots of fu
10 Someone who makes things out of wood